Best Handwriting for

We hope that you enjoy working through this book.

2

How to sit for handwriting.

Are we mad?

You already know how to sit, don't you?

Of course you know how to sit,
but there are some important rules for handwriting:

- ✓ Sit comfortably at your table, so that you can see each letter as you write.
- ✓ Hold your paper still.
- ✓ Make sure that your table is tidy. You need plenty of space to work.
- ✓ Hold your pen or pencil like this:

if you are right-handed ...   and like this if you are left-handed.

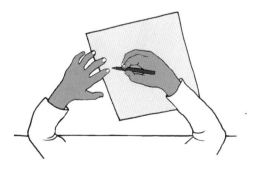

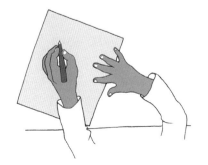

3

Here's the first letter to practise.

Start writing here.

Write the letter c all across the page:

c c c c c

Try to keep every letter c the same size.
Make sure you start each one at the top.

Letter o is very like the letter c. It starts in the same place, but finishes there as well.

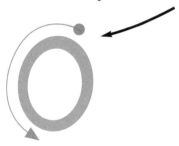

Start and finish here.

o o o o o

Letter a is also like the letter c .It starts in the same place, but then finishes with a straight line and a tail to join from.

a a a a a

When we join from an a or a c we do a slope upwards.

When we join from an o we do a bridge join across.

slope join

ac

slope join

co

bridge join

oc

Try the joins yourself:

ac ac ac ac

ca ca ca

oc oc oc

oa oa oa

Now try this word:

slope   bridge   slope   bridge

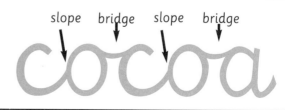

cocoa

cocoa

Here are two more letters that start in the same way as letter a.

Letter d is called an ascender because it goes upwards.

Practise letter a and letter d. Make sure that letter d is taller.

a d a d a d

Letter g is called a descender because it goes downwards.

Letter g goes below the line:

g g g

Try to keep each letter g the same size.

Letter s starts like a letter c but then wiggles the other way.

Look:

Keep the letter s the same height as the letter c.

s c s c s c

Letter e has two shapes.

We use this one at the start of a word or when we join from a bridge join.

We use this one when we join from a slope join.

Try these:

ec ec ec

ce ce ce

We don't mind joining <u>to</u> letter g or letter s...

... but we are not joining <u>from</u> them in this book.

Practise joining <u>to</u> letters g and s:

eg   ag   og   es   as   os   ds   eg   ag   og   es   as   os   ds

Now practise these words, without joining <u>from</u> letters g and s.

gas gas

dogs dogs

age age

ages ages

cages cages

egg egg

Be very careful with the size of each letter.
Do your words look just like these?

gas   dogs   age   ages   cages   egg

8

Letters l, i and h...

...all start with a downward line.

Practise each letter:

l l l l l

i i i i i

h h h h h

Look how we join a letter i to a letter l:

Just keep going with the slope of the letter l.

Try this word:

gill gill gill

9

This is a bridge join to a tall letter:

oh

Remember that a tall letter is called an ascender.

This is a slope join to an ascender:

eh

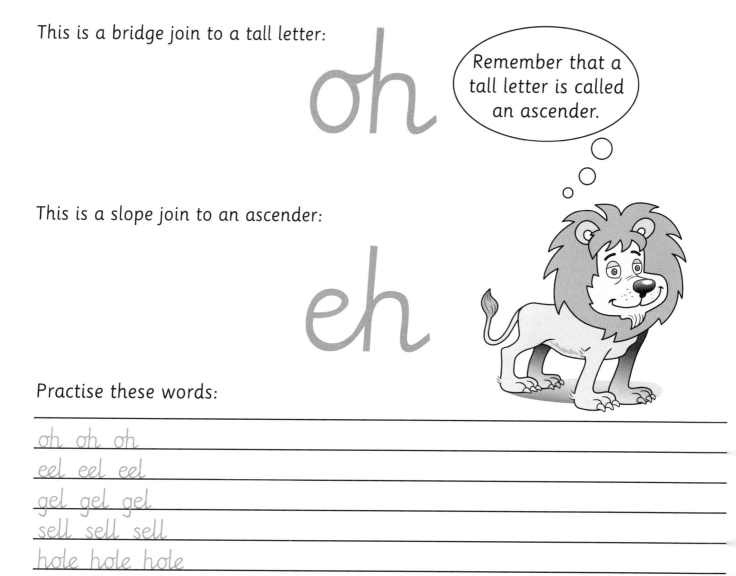

Practise these words:

oh oh oh

eel eel eel

gel gel gel

sell sell sell

hole hole hole

Make sure that your ascenders are taller than the other letters.

Letter m and letter n are made in the same way as letter h...

... but they are not ascenders.

h m n

Practise the letters.

m m m m m

n n n n n

Now try these words.

ham ham ham

name name name

some some some

come come come

coming coming coming

cone cone cone

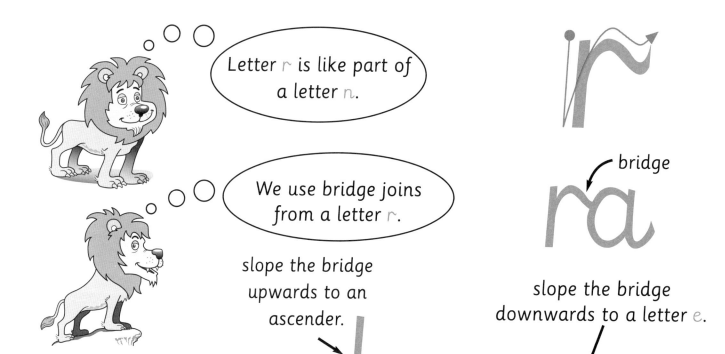

Letter r is like part of a letter n.

We use bridge joins from a letter r.

bridge

slope the bridge upwards to an ascender.

slope the bridge downwards to a letter e.

Practise these:

ra ro re rl

rain rain rain

rear rear rear

roll roll roll

girl girl girl

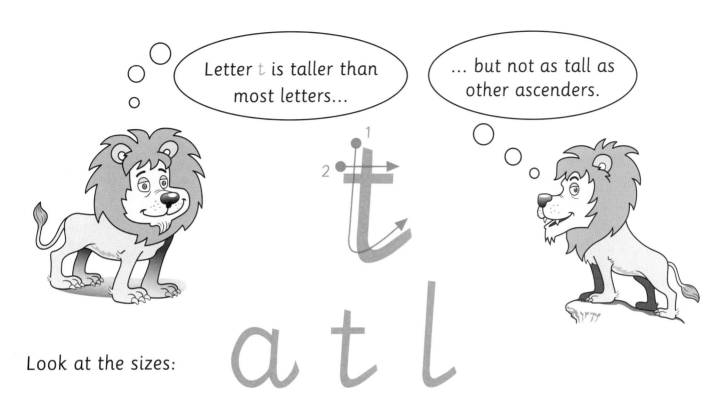

Look at the sizes:

Try these words:

tree tree tree

smart smart smart

gate gate gate

If letter t is at the beginning of a word, or in the middle, write the whole word then go back and cross the letter t.

tell tell tell

letter letter letter

Letter b is quite like a letter h.

We start with a downward line.

Because we finish here we are not going to join to the next letter.

Letter b is an ascender so it needs to be tall.

Practise the letter b.

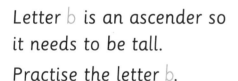

b b b b b

Now try these words:

bob bob bob
bobbing bobbing bobbing
able able able
table table table
nibble nibble nibble

We are going to learn a new way to write letter k.

Old way   New way

You can write the new letter k without taking your pencil off the paper.

Letter k is an ascender. Compare the size of the letter k to the size of a letter a.

We can join to and from a letter k.

k k k k k

oak oak oak

like like like

Letter p is quite like a letter b.

But it is a descender not an ascender.

Because we finish here we are not going to join to the next letter.

Practise the letter p:

p p p p p

Now practise some words.

pop pop pop
stop stop stop
lap lap lap
lip lip lip
apple apple apple
please please please

We can join <u>to</u> a letter f.

We can join <u>from</u> a letter f using its crossbar.

Letter f is as tall as a letter l.
Letter f is a descender as well.

Look carefully at the joins:

fa fl fe

fa fa fa fa fa
fl fl fl fl fl
fe fe fe fe fe

In this book we are not joining <u>from</u> the letter j or the letter y but we do join <u>to</u> them.

jelly jelly jelly

smelly jelly

jam jam jam

smelly jam and jelly

major major major

pyjamas pyjamas pyjamas

18

Normally letter q is followed by letter u.

We are not joining from here in this book.

Letter q is a descender.

q q q q q

u u u u u

qu qu qu qu qu

Now try some words:

quick quick quick

quite quite quite

quiet quiet quiet

Practise this sentence:

You must be quite quiet.

Letter u is not always behind letter q.

Practise this word:

umbrella umbrella umbrella

Now check your words:

✳ Is each letter l the same height as the letter b?

✳ Are the letter b and the letter l taller than the other letters?

✳ Are these letters all the same height? u m r e a

Here are some more words to practise.

under   up   put   butter   bucket   cup

'Double u' is a strange name for a letter w.

'Double v' would be better.

Practise the letters. Keep them all the same size.

v v v v v

w w w w w

Try these words:

wet wet wet

wave cave save gave give weave

new dew cow how now with awful

Now try this sentence:

Show me the view.

Letter x is made by drawing two crossing lines.

In this book we join <u>to</u> it but not <u>from</u> it.

ex ax

Look:

Practise some letters:

x x x

Now some words:

axe fox fax next
next six sixteen
luxury mixture box

Letter z is made by one continuous line.

I'm joining <u>to</u> the letter z but not <u>from</u> it.

gaze

Practice makes perfect.

z z z z z

gaze gaze gaze

amaze amaze amaze

zoo zebra

There are zebras in the zoo.

Queen Elizabeth the First was a powerful lady.

CAPITAL LETTERS

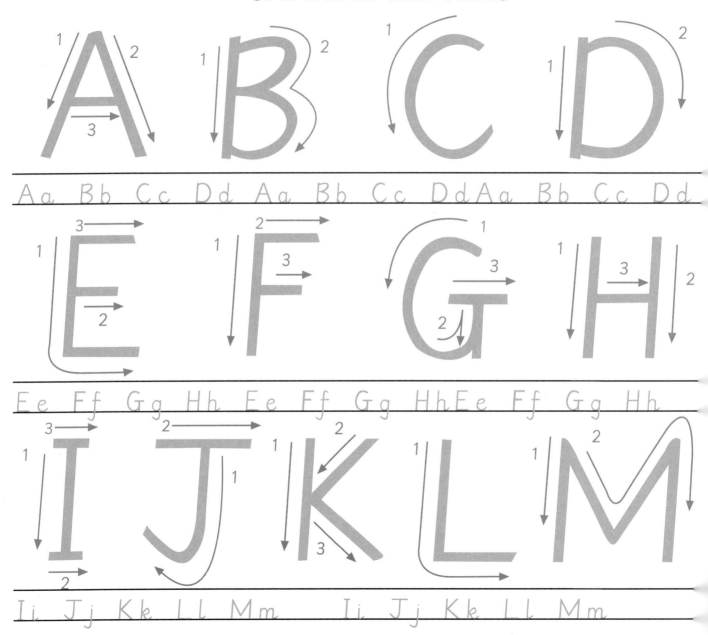

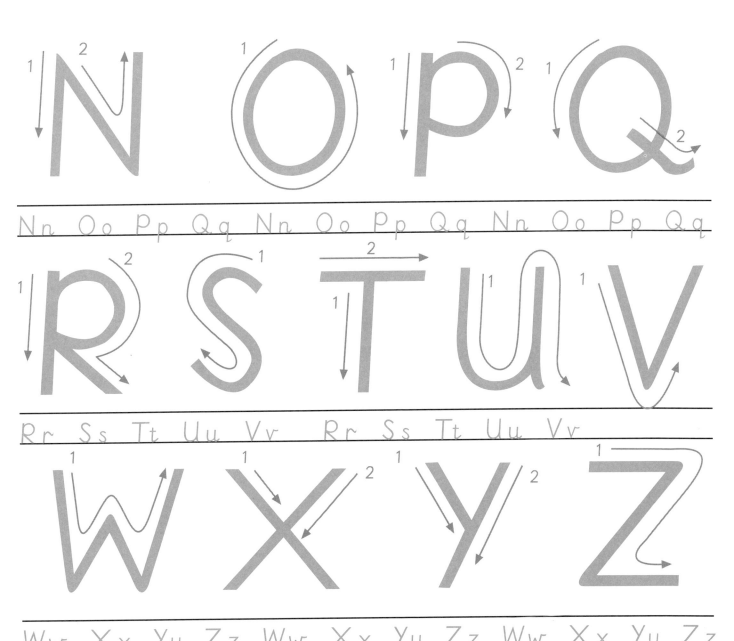

Nn Oo Pp Qq Nn Oo Pp Qq Nn Oo Pp Qq

Rr Ss Tt Uu Vv Rr Ss Tt Uu Vv

Ww Xx Yy Zz Ww Xx Yy Zz Ww Xx Yy Zz

25

NUMERALS

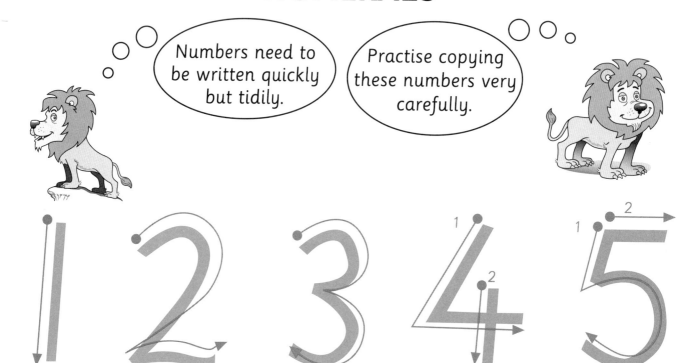

Numbers need to be written quickly but tidily.

Practise copying these numbers very carefully.

MONEY, MONEY, MONEY

Some people find the pound sign difficult to write.

It's easy if you just follow our instructions.

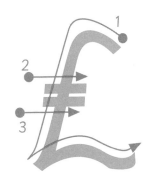

Practise writing a row of pound signs.
Try to keep them all the same size.

£ £ £ £ £

Here are some other important money signs:

The euro

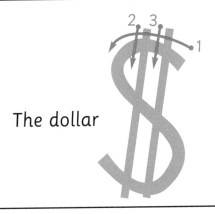

The dollar

€ $ € $ € $

PUNCTUATION MARKS

Look very carefully at the comma and full stop in the sentence below.

They only need to be very small marks, but they must be clear.

I wore my shorts, T-shirt and football boots.

The comma is just big enough to cross the line.

The full stop is just above the line.

Practise these sentences on lined paper. Make sure that your handwriting is tidy. Don't forget the punctuation marks.

One, two, three, four, someone is knocking at my door.

I need some paper, a pencil and a ruler.

I like animals. I have books about whales, cats and dogs.

Now write four sentences of your own.

We use speech marks when we write down what someone says.

They only need to be small, but they need to be clear.

"Hello."

The full stop is written <u>before</u> the second set of speech marks.

Speech marks are written with short, simple strokes. Speech marks should be at the same height as the tops of the ascenders.

"I have got my sandwiches," said Jasdeep.
"Don't forget your drink," added her mum.

Copy out the short conversation between Jasdeep and her mum. Make sure that the speech marks curve inwards slightly. Remember that the comma is written before the second set of speech marks.

Now try this short conversation:

"I am going swimming," said Jack.
"I'm coming too," Sarah responded.

MORE PUNCTUATION MARKS

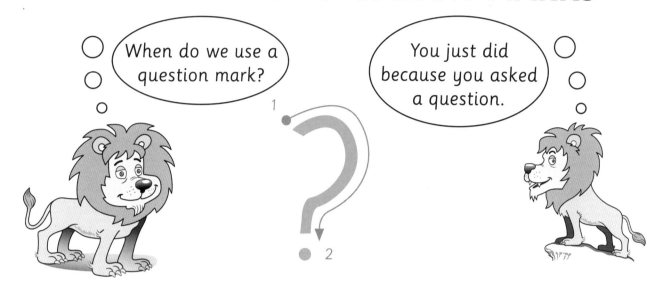

Copy these question words and question marks:

What? Where? Who? When? Why? How?

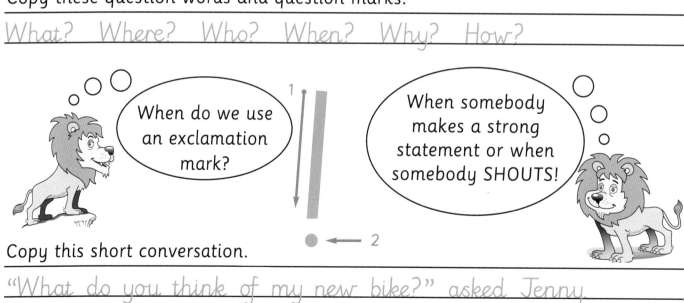

Copy this short conversation.

"What do you think of my new bike?" asked Jenny.
"Wow! It's great!" replied Jess.

Here is a poem by Judy Richardson.

Clickety clack,
The wheels on the track
Rumble along,
Singing their song .
Faster and faster,
Leaving the station,
Taking the people
Across the nation .
Rushing with speed,
Past field and farm .
Shooting through tunnels,
Sound the alarm .
Begin to slow down,
Approaching the town
Arriving back,
Clickety clack.

Copy it very carefully, in your best handwriting.

You've reached the end of the book.

Well done. Your last job is to copy out some rules for good handwriting.

Our bullet points are made from a star like this.

You can use bullet points if you want to.

☆ I will use my best handwriting for important work.
☆ I will try to keep the letters the right size.
☆ The ascenders will be tall, but not too tall. The descenders will go through the line, but not too far. The other letters will all be the same size.
☆ I will always keep my desk tidy.